The Dino Pals

123 ABC

Illustrated by Jan Lewis

BACKPACK BOOKS

NEW YORK

1 One huge dinosaur going for a walk.

2 Two tiny dinosaurs stop to talk.

3 Three tall dinosaurs munching in the trees.

4 Four dinosaurs with horns and knobby knees.

5 Five frisky
dinosaurs
having lots
of fun.

6 Six spiky dinosaurs standing in the sun.

7 Seven mommy dinosaurs looking after eggs.

8 Eight daddy dinosaurs with very long legs.

9 Nine prowling dinosaurs, as hungry as can be.

Can you count...

1 Silly dinosaur

2 eyes

3 tail spikes

4 legs

5 flowers

6 leaves

7 stripes

8 spots

9 eggs

10 teeth

A is for Apatosaurus and apple.

B is for Baryonyx and bat.

C is for Carnotaurus and claw.

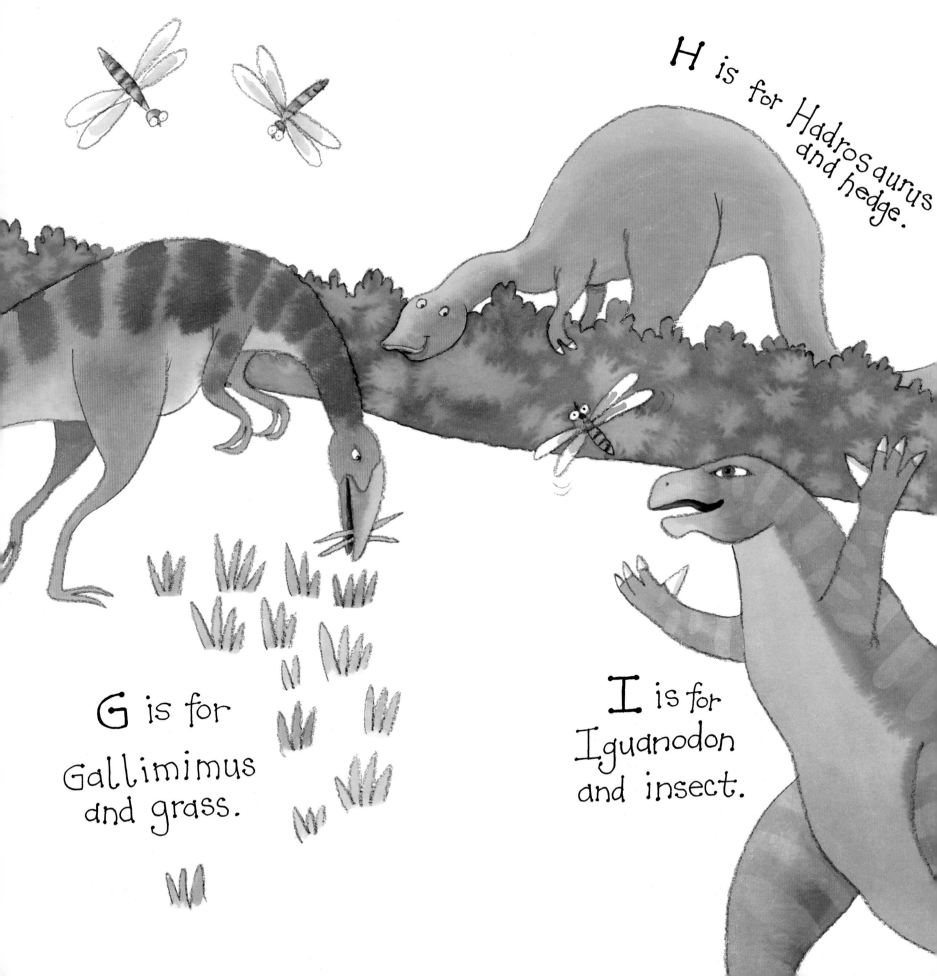

H is for Hadrosaurus and hedge.

G is for Gallimimus and grass.

I is for Iguanodon and insect.

N is for Nodosaurus and nuts.

M is for Monoclonius and melons.

O is for Oviraptor and oranges.

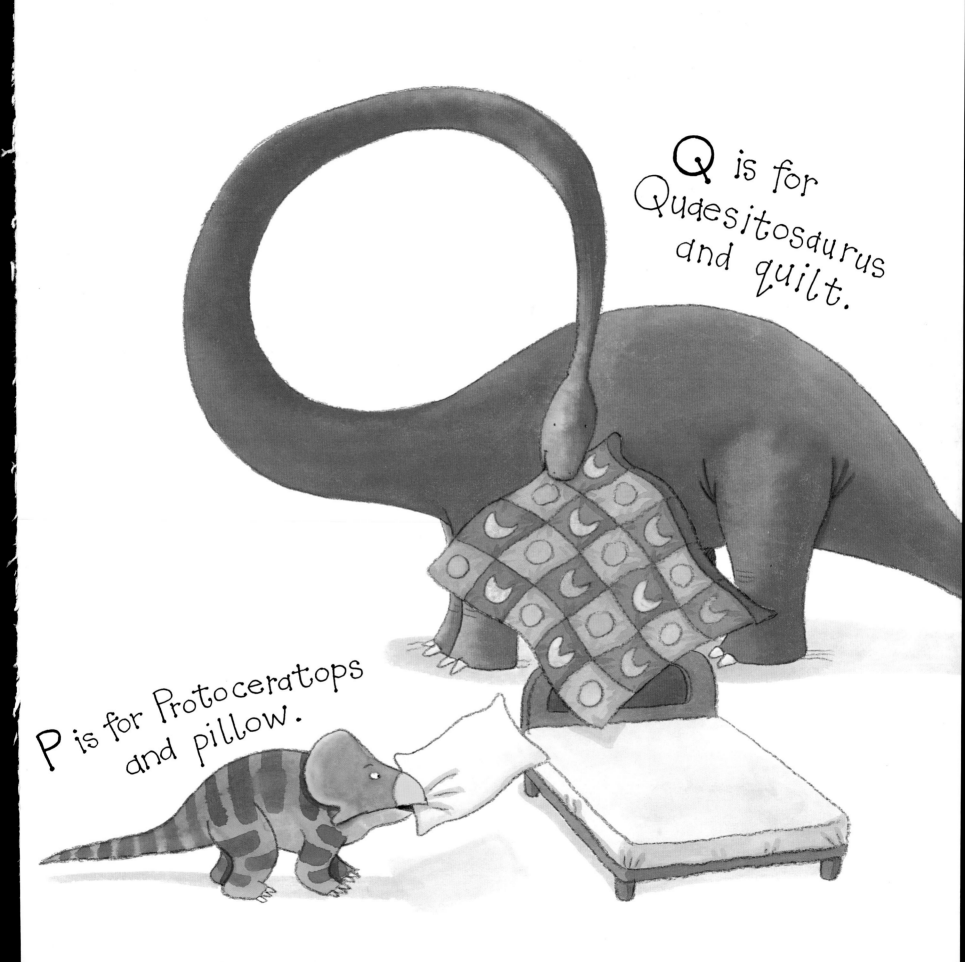

Q is for Quaesitosaurus and quilt.

P is for Protoceratops and pillow.

U is for Ultrasaurus and umbrella.

V is for Velociraptor and volcano.

W is for Wannanosaurus and wall.